BIG BEAR

AND THE LOST LAMB

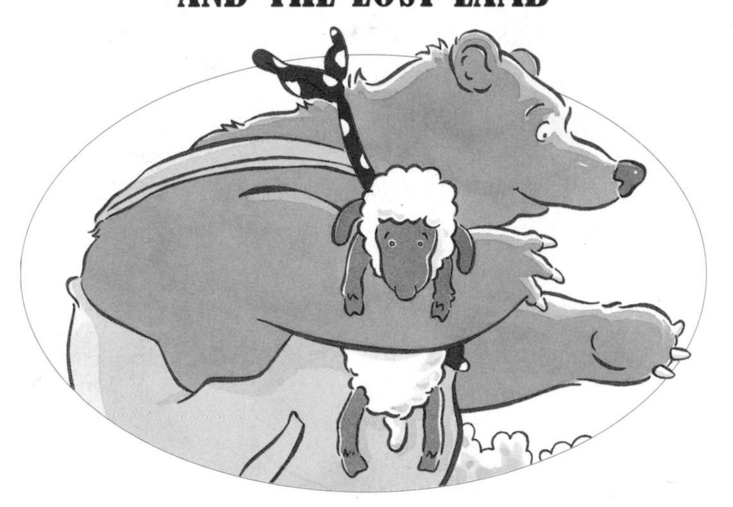
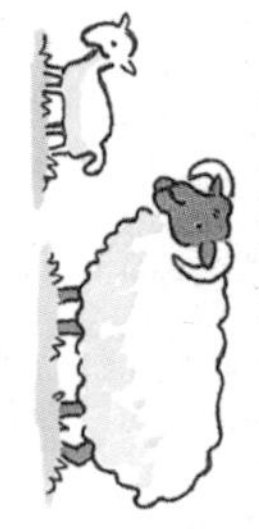

Written by Dugald Steer

Illustrated by John Blackman

Big Bear and Morris Mouse are going for a walk. What is this? Why, it is a little lost **lamb**!

Where are your
friends, little **lamb**?

Big Bear and Morris Mouse
take the little **lamb** to the farm.
Do your friends live here,
little **lamb**?

PERCY'S
FARM

Big Bear is looking in the farmyard. Cluck! Cluck! Cluck! Are these your friends, little **lamb**?
No, Big Bear. Those are **chickens** with their little **chicks**.

Big Bear is looking in the farmyard. Moo! Moo! Moo! Are these your friends, little **lamb**?

No, Big Bear. This is a **cow** with her little **calf**.

Big Bear is looking in the farmyard. Whinny! Whinny! Whinny! Are these your friends little **lamb**?

No, Big Bear. This is a **horse** with her little **foal**.

Big Bear is looking in the lane.
Cackle! Cackle! Cackle!
Are these your friends,
little **lamb**?

No, Big Bear. This is a **goose** with her little **goslings**.

Big Bear is looking on the hillside. Bleat! Bleat! Bleat! Are these your little friends **lamb**?

No, Big Bear.
This is a **goat**
with her little **kids**.

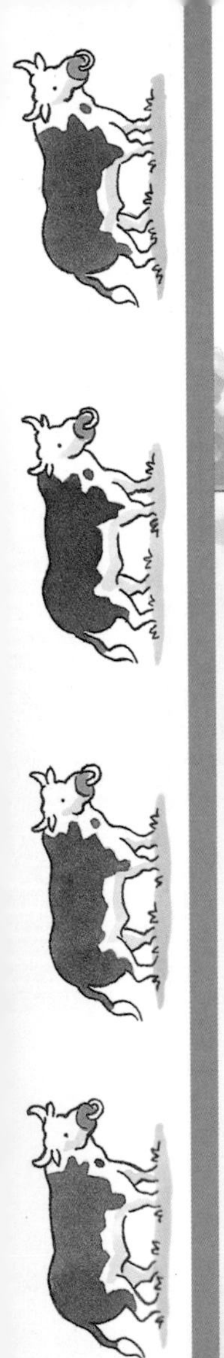

Big Bear is looking in
the field. Snort! Snort! Snort!
Is that your friend, little **lamb**?
No, Big Bear! That is a **bull**!
LOOK OUT!

BAM!

Big Bear is looking in the field.
Baa! Baa! Baa!

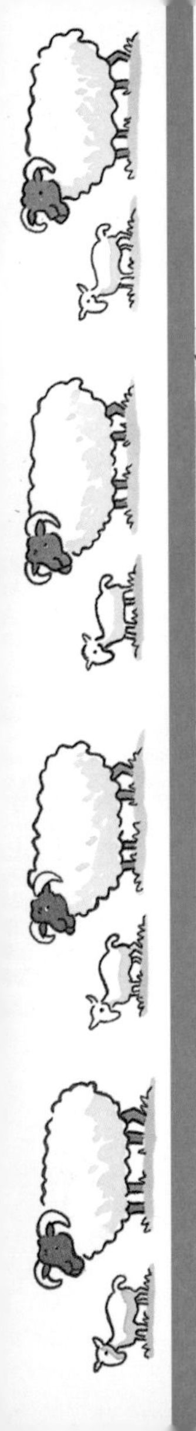

Are those your friends, little **lamb**?

Yes, Big Bear! Those are **sheep** with their little **lambs**.

Here is Percy Pig! And look!
The little **lamb** has found
his friends at last.

This is a Parragon Book.

Parragon
13-17 Avonbridge Trading Estate,
Atlantic Road, Avonmouth, Bristol. BS11 9QD

Produced by The Templar Company plc,
Pippbrook Mill, London Road, Dorking, Surrey RH4 1JE.

Designed by Janie Louise Hunt
Printed and bound in Italy
ISBN 0-75251-498-9